# THE JAGS

D0716248

## Up for the Cup

# TOM WATT

## RISING★STARS

**Rising Stars UK Ltd.**
22 Grafton Street, London W1S 4EX
www.risingstars-uk.com

Text, design and layout © 2009 Rising Stars Uk Ltd.
The right of Tom Watt to be identified as the author of this work has been
asserted by him in accordance with the Copyright, Design and Patents Act,
1988.

Published 2009

Publisher: Gill Budgell
Editor: Jane Wood
Text design and typesetting: Clive Sutherland
Illustrator: Michael Emmerson for Advocate Art
Cover design: Burville-Riley Partnership
Cover photograph: Ron Coello at www.coellophotography.co.uk
With special thanks to; Robert Dye, Harry Garner, Tyrone Smith, Lewis
McKenzie, Kobina Crankson and Alex Whyte

British Library Cataloguing in Publication Data.
A CIP record for this book is available from the British Library.

ISBN: 978-1-84680-486-1

Printed in the UK by CPI Bookmarque, Croydon, CR0 4TD

**Mixed Sources**
Product group from well-managed
forests and other controlled sources
www.fsc.org  Cert no. TT-COC-002227
© 1996 Forest Stewardship Council

# Contents

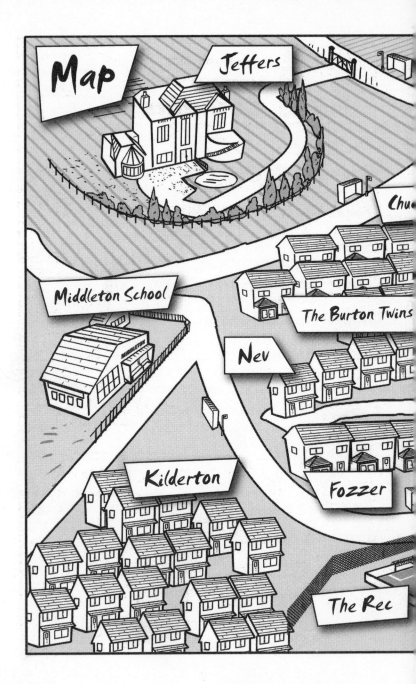

Map

Jeffers

Chu[c...]

Middleton School

The Burton Twins

Nev

Kilderton

Fozzer

The Rec

# Meet the Jags

**Andy**

**Name:** Andrew Burton

**Fact:** He's the Jags' captain.

**Loves:** Spurs

**FYI:** The Jags may be his mates, but they'd better not forget he's the Skipper.

**Burts**

**Name:** Terry Burton

**Fact:** He's Andy's twin brother.

**Loves:** Football, football, and more football. He's football crazy!

**FYI:** He's a big Arsenal fan.

**Dev**

**Name:** Ryan Devlin

**Fact:** He's very forgetful.

**Loves:** Daydreaming!

**FYI:** He's always covered in mud and bruises.

Fozzer

**Name:** Hamed Foster

**Fact:** He can run like crazy, but he shoots like crazy too – sometimes at the wrong goal!

**Loves:** Telling bad jokes.

**FYI:** His best friend is Nev.

Keeps

**Name:** Jim Ward

**Fact:** He's the Jags' Number One goalie – whether he likes it or not!

**Loves:** Trying to score from his end of the pitch.

**FYI:** He's the tallest member of the Jags.

Jeffers

**Name:** Jeffrey Gilfoyle Chapman

**Fact:** He's the only one of the Jags who doesn't live on the Chudley Park estate.

**Loves:** Being in the Jags.

**FYI:** He's the Jags' top goal-scorer.

7

**Nev**

**Name:** Denton Neville

**Fact:** Nev is the Jags' most talented player.

**Loves:** Fozzer's bad jokes.

**FYI:** He keeps his feet on the ground and always looks out for his football crazy mates.

**Mrs Burton**

**Name:** Pam Burton

**Fact:** The Burton twins' mum, and a team 'mum' for all the Jags.

**Loves:** Sorting out her boys.

**FYI:** Doesn't actually like football!

**Mr Ward**

**Name:** Jack Ward

**Fact:** He's Jim's dad and the Jags' coach!

**Loves:** Going on and on, doing his team talks.

**FYI:** He's taking his coaching exams.

# Who's Marking Who?

*Every team loses games. Every player makes mistakes. I know you have to just get up and get on with it. But sometimes it's not that easy.*

**Fozzer**   Dev! Dev!

**Dev**   All right! I hear you!

**Fozzer**    No. That's the boy you should be marking.

**Dev**    No. He's yours. Get back!

**Fozzer**    You do it!

**Dev**    Oh, no!

**Fozzer**    That's 2–0. We'll never come back now.

**Dev**     Why didn't you mark him?

**Fozzer**  Why didn't *you* mark him, you
            mean. You're so slow, Dev. He's
            beating you every time!

**Dev**     I'm slow? Why is it always me?

**Fozzer**  Well, no time to worry now. Let's
            get on with the game.

We lost the match 3–0 and Mr Ward, the Jags coach, seemed to blame me.

**Fozzer**     Hey, Dev. Do you know why your mum would never have Ronaldo round for dinner?

**Dev**     Eh?

**Fozzer**     Because he can't stop dribbling. You know – Ronaldo. He's always dribbling!

**Dev**      I get it, Fozzer. I just don't think it's very funny.

**Fozzer**      What about this one? What part of a football ground is never the same?

**Dev**      Um, the changing room. I saw that one in my comic last week. Fozzer, no jokes for a minute, please.

13

**Fozzer**    All right. Only a minute, though. What's up?

**Dev**    Did you think I played badly today?

**Fozzer**    No worse than usual, mate. You're a good player. Everybody knows that. It's just …

**Dev**    Just what? Tell me, Fozzer.

**Fozzer**  It's just that sometimes you don't seem to be thinking about the game.

**Dev**  Was it my fault we lost today? That's what Mr Ward was saying.

**Fozzer**  No, he wasn't. He was just talking about the second goal. Come on, your minute's up. What's a bank manager's favourite type of football match?

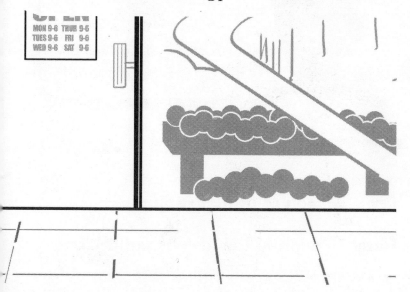

MON 9-6  THUR 9-6
TUES 9-6  FRI 9-6
WED 9-6  SAT 9-6

# In the Dumps

The answer is *fiver – side*, in case you're wondering. *Fiver – side*. Get it? Like money. Anyway, me and Dev went to the Rec after the game. He was really down.

**Dev**  You're right, I suppose.

**Fozzer**  I know. I'm always right. What are we talking about?

**Dev**     About why I let the team down.

**Fozzer**  You didn't let the team down.

**Dev**     No? But you said that sometimes I'm not thinking about the game.

**Fozzer**  Well, we all do that a bit. I never know when I'm going to think of a joke. Sometimes it's in the middle of a match.

**Dev**    But what should I do?

**Fozzer**    Do what you always do. That was a great goal you scored last week.

**Dev**    I don't think I'll get the chance. I think Mr Ward might leave me out of the five-a-side tournament next week.

**Fozzer**    He won't do that. We're all together. We're the Jags.

**Dev**      Yeah, maybe. But what about that goal today? He said it was down to me.

**Fozzer**   I bet he's forgotten all about it by now.

**Dev**      Well, I haven't. He was right. I don't know why I didn't mark that striker.

**Fozzer**   You thought I was marking him! Look, Dev, I bet Mr Ward has forgotten. You should as well. It will all be okay tomorrow.

**Dev** Do you think so?

**Fozzer** Yes. Now, come on, let's play. If you don't kick the ball to me, I'll tell you a joke! A really bad one, too.

**Dev** What? Sorry, Fozzer. I was thinking about the five-a-sides next Sunday.

**Fozzer** There you go again! Miles away! Well, I warned you! Next joke, coming up. What should a manager do if the pitch is flooded? Bring on his subs, of course! Now, pass me the ball!

# Our Name on the Cup

*Dev and I go to different schools. I go to Middleton. He's at Parkside. Sometimes we meet up after school.*

**Dev**  Hi, Fozzer. Are you off out?

**Fozzer**  No. I'm going round to my auntie's house. I'll get two dinners tonight. Fish and chips at Auntie Jackie's and then whatever Mum gets for me later. Two puddings as well!

**Dev**    Where do you put it all? Have you got hollow legs?

**Fozzer**    Hollow legs? That's good, Dev. Here's one. What do you call the room where they keep school dinners?

**Dev**     I don't know. Our dinners come on a van.

**Fozzer**  No, no. It's a joke. Where do they keep school dinners? In a *mush* – room, of course.

**Dev**     Oh, yeah. I see. Hey, Fozzer, what about the five-a-sides at the weekend? I was talking to Keeps today. I asked him if his dad was still angry with me about the goal last week.

**Fozzer**   What did he say?

**Dev**   He said his dad wasn't angry in the first place. He was just trying to talk about what happened.

**Fozzer**   I told you not to worry.

**Dev**   I know you did. Keeps said his dad doesn't mind when we lose. It gives him something to talk to us about.

**Fozzer**    Maybe we should lose a few more games, then. Just to keep Mr Ward happy!

**Dev**    Do you want to know the best bit?

**Fozzer**    What?

**Dev**    Mr Ward wants all of us there on Sunday. Even though it's five-a-side, he wants a full squad.

**Fozzer**    So, you were never going to be left out, after all?

**Dev**    No. I suppose not. We're all in it together. Like always!

# Splinters

*There were five other teams on Sunday. So the Jags had five games. The overall winner would take home the cup. Mr Ward called out the team to start the first game.*

**Fozzer**   Hey, Dev. Looks like you and me on the bench. Come on. I'll tell you some jokes while we wait for our turn!

**Dev**   I think I'd rather do a warm-up.
I must have heard all your jokes
by now, Fozzer.

**Fozzer**   Okay, Dev. What do you call a
man with a toilet on his head?

**Dev**   Lou. See? I told you I'd heard
them all.

**Fozzer**    Ah, yes. But what do you call a *woman* with *two* toilets on her head?

**Dev**    What are you on about, Fozzer?

**Fozzer**    Lulu! Get it? Loo – loo?

**Dev**    Shh! It's time for kick-off. Let's watch. We have to be ready to go on if Mr Ward calls us.

**Fozzer**   Come on, Jeffers. You can do it.
Get us a hat-trick!

**Dev**   Do you think Jeffers is our best
player?

**Fozzer**   He's the best goal-scorer,
maybe. But I think Nev's the
best all-round player.

**Dev**   Yes, maybe. But what about Andy? He always wins the ball. He's a good skipper, too.

**Fozzer**   That's true. But haven't you forgotten somebody?

**Dev**   Well, Burts tries hard. And Keeps is the number one in goal.

**Fozzer**   I wasn't thinking of them, Dev. Shoot, Nev! Oh, unlucky.

**Dev**    Who, then?

**Fozzer**    What about me and you?

**Dev**    Well, we're on the bench. That says it all. Good ball, Burts. Go on, Nev!

**Fozzer**    Don't be silly. We're not subs because we're not good players.

**Dev**    Well, why then? I know Mr Ward will have picked his best team.

**Fozzer**    No, you're wrong. We are the Jags' secret weapons. Fozzer and Dev: the Twin Terrors. Every coach needs players who can change the game. That's us!

**Dev**    I'm not so sure. But never mind. Look! Go on, Jeffers!

**Fozzer**   Shoot, Jeffers!

**Dev**   Yes! Goal! That's 1–0 to the Jags!

**Fozzer**   Great goal, lads! Come on, Mr Ward. Isn't it time to bring on a couple of subs?

**Dev**   What? When we're winning? I think we may be on this bench for a while, Fozzer.

# Twin Terrors!

Mr Ward kept the same team until the end of the game. The Jags won 2–0. I'd almost run out of jokes. And Dev was starting to think we were going to be subs for the rest of the day.

**Dev**  See, Fozzer? I told you. I bet we don't even get a game.

**Fozzer**      Why is Mr Ward waving to us, then?

**Dev**      We must be going on for the second game. Come on, Fozzer!

**Fozzer**      Mr Ward must think we're good players after all, eh? What did I tell you?

*The game started. I was so keen to do well that I was running all over the place. Maybe I was a bit too keen.*

**Fozzer**   Dev! Pass!

**Dev**      I'm okay. I can dribble it out of here.

**Fozzer**   No! Pass!

**Dev**      Oh, no! I didn't see him there.

**Fozzer**   Dev! What are you doing, mate? You fouled him!

**Dev**      I got the ball!

**Fozzer**   Oh, yeah? So why has the ref given a penalty?

*We were 1–0 down and it was all my fault. Again. I was sure Mr Ward was going to sub me. But when I looked at him, he shouted out: "Unlucky, Dev! Keep going!" So that's what I did.*

**Fozzer**     Come on, Dev. Let's try and do something!

**Dev**          Sorry, Fozzer. I should have listened to you.

**Fozzer**     Don't worry. Just play.

**Dev**     Thanks, mate. What did you say
         we were? The Twin Terrors? Let's
         go!

**Fozzer**  Great tackle, Dev. Now pass.

**Dev**     Keep going. I'm in the box.

**Fozzer**  Try a volley. Here comes the ball.

**Dev**     Got it! Yes!

**Fozzer**  Yes! Back of the net, Dev!
         Brilliant!

**Dev**     Great pass, Fozzer.

**Fozzer**  Just look at Mr Ward's face. I bet he's happy we're in the team now!

**Dev**     I am, too! This is only the start, though. We can win this game, you know.

And that's what we did. Burts got a couple of goals to make it 3–1 to us. In the end, we came second in the tournament. We lost one and drew two of our other three games. But it didn't matter. We had a great time.

**Dev**   Thanks for bringing us,
          Mr Ward.

**Fozzer** Look, Dev. That woman has got
          something for you. It's a little
          cup. What does it say?

**Dev**   See for yourself. Valley Road
          Five-a-side Goal of the Day.
          Great! Come on the Jags!

# JAGUARS 1 HOPE WOOD 1

*Our last game in the five-a-side tournament was against Hope Wood. If we won the game, we would win the cup. If Hope Wood won the game, they would win the cup.*

**Fozzer**  I don't understand it, Dev. What happens if it's a draw?

**Dev**  Don't worry, Fozzer. All we have to do is our best.

**Fozzer**    Well, at least we're both playing.

**Dev**    Get back, Fozzer.

**Fozzer**    Oh, no. I didn't see him coming!
That's 1–0 to Hope Wood.

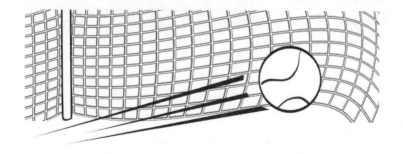

**Dev**     Come on, Fozzer. Let's make up for it. There's a minute to go.

**Fozzer**  Pass it inside, Dev.

**Dev**     Good goal, Fozzer! That's 1–1.

*It was great! We came second in the five-a-side tournament. But sometimes you don't even have to win for it to feel like you have!*

# Five-a-side Special

Five-a-side football is really fun. It is played on a small pitch with small goals. The ball has to stay below head height. It is very skilful.

The Jags train at the Rec. The Rec is set up like a five-a-side pitch. That helps make sure that the Jags are all good on the ball. They're fit, too. It's a small pitch, but you have to keep moving. There's no time to rest!

Premier League players play 11-a-side football. But they often play five-a-side games in training. The ball moves very quickly, which keeps the players sharp. The coach may say they can only touch the ball once or twice. If they touch it more than that, the other team gets a free kick.

When you watch the Premier League teams play, you often see them do little moves that they have learned during five-a-side games.

# Five-a-side Quiz

## Questions

1 What kind of pitch is five-a-side played on?

2 Why do the players rarely head the ball in five-a-side?

3 Why is five-a-side good training for top players?

4 How many a side is Premier League football?

## Answers

1 A small pitch.
2 Because the ball must not go over head height.
3 It keeps them sharp.
4 11-a-side.

46

# About the Author

Tom Watt, who wrote the Jags books, used to play a lot of five-a-side football. He is a bit too old for it now! The fewer players there are in each team, the more the players have to run around.

One time, Tom played one-versus-two, against his son and his son's friend. He could hardly walk afterwards!

# THE JAGS

## RISING ★ STARS

**The Jags books are available from most book sellers.**

**For mail order information
please call Rising Stars on 0871 47 23 01 0
or visit www.risingstars-uk.com**